Glencoe
Algebra 1

**Integration
Applications
Connections**

Investigations and Projects Masters

GLENCOE
McGraw-Hill

New York, New York   Columbus, Ohio   Woodland Hills, California   Peoria, Illinois

Glencoe/McGraw-Hill

A Division of The **McGraw·Hill** *Companies*

Send all inquiries to:
Glencoe/McGraw-Hill
8787 Orion Place
Columbus, OH 43240

Algebra I
Investigations and Projects Masters

ISBN: 0-02-824860-0

9 10 021 03 02 01 00

Contents

Investigations   **Page**

The Greenhouse Effect (Chapters 2 and 3)
Teacher Notes 1
Scoring Guide 3
Recording Sheet 4

Go Fish! (Chapters 4 and 5)
Teacher Notes 5
Scoring Guide 7
Recording Sheet 8

Smoke Gets in Your Eyes (Chapters 6 and 7)
Teacher Notes 9
Scoring Guide 11
Recording Sheet 12

Ready, Set, Drop! (Chapters 8 and 9)
Teacher Notes 13
Scoring Guide 15
Recording Sheet 16

The Brickyard (Chapters 10 and 11)
Teacher Notes 17
Scoring Guide 19
Recording Sheet 20

A Growing Concern (Chapters 12 and 13)
Teacher Notes 21
Scoring Guide 23
Recording Sheet 24

Chapter Projects   **Page**

Chapter 1 Project A: The "Write" Way
Student Page 25
Parent Letter 26

Chapter 1 Project B: Statistically Speaking
Student Page 27
Parent Letter 28

Chapter 2 Project A: Good for You!
Student Page 29
Parent Letter 30

Chapter 2 Project B: Game Time
Student Page 31
Parent Letter 32

Chapter 3 Project A: Higher Learning
Student Page 33
Parent Letter 34

Chapter 3 Project B: Numbering Systems
Student Page 35
Parent Letter 36

Chapter 4 Project A: A World of Names
Student Page 37
Parent Letter 38

Chapter 4 Project B: Such a Deal . . .
Student Page 39
Parent Letter 40

Chapter 5 Project A: Venues and Revenues
Student Page 41
Parent Letter 42

Chapter 5 Project B: Raising Funds
Student Page 43
Parent Letter 44

Chapter 6 Project A: Analyzing Immigration
Student Page 45
Parent Letter 46

Chapter 6 Project B: Growing Graphs
Student Page 47
Parent Letter 48

Chapter 7 Project A: Choose a Career
Student Page 49
Parent Letter 50

Chapter 7 Project B: Healthy Ranges
Student Page 51
Parent Letter 52

Chapter 8 Project A: Games People Play
Student Page 53
Parent Letter 54

Chapter 8 Project B: Linear Thinking
Student Page 55
Parent Letter 56

Chapter 9 Project A: Make History
Student Page 57
Parent Letter 58

Chapter 9 Project B: Endangered Species
Student Page 59
Parent Letter 60

Chapter 10 Project A: Movie Numbers
Student Page 61
Parent Letter 62

Chapter 10 Project B: Formulas for Success
Student Page 63
Parent Letter 64

Chapter 11 Project A: Volunteer Survey
Student Page 65
Parent Letter 66

Chapter 11 Project B: Constructing Parabolas
Student Page 67
Parent Letter 68

Chapter 12 Project A: Mayan Time
Student Page 69
Parent Letter 70

Chapter 12 Project B: Get Focused!
Student Page 71
Parent Letter 72

Chapter 13 Project A: Radical Survey
Student Page 73
Parent Letter 74

Chapter 13 Project B: Spirals
Student Page 75
Parent Letter 76

Overview

This booklet contains a variety of useful information for teachers, students, and parents.

Investigation Masters are designed for use with the six Investigations in the Student Edition. Two pages of Teacher Notes provide a description of each Investigation and its follow-up activities, as well as a list of mathematical objectives for the Investigation, information on how to conduct the Investigation, and a list of outside resources. A Scoring Guide is provided to help with assessment. This should be shared with students at the beginning of the Investigation so they are aware of assessment strategies. There is also a Recording Sheet for students to use as they work on each Investigation.

Chapter Project A Masters consist of two pages for each chapter in the Student Edition. The first page provides students with directions and suggestions for completing a project that relates to the information in the corresponding chapter opener in the Student Edition. The second page contains a letter that can be reproduced and sent to parents to inform them about the requirements of the project. Parents are asked to sign and return a form at the bottom of each Parent Letter.

Chapter Project B Masters also consist of a student page and a Parent Letter for each chapter in the Student Edition. These masters differ from the Chapter Project A Masters in that the projects they describe are related to the mathematics of Student Edition chapters but not to the information in the chapter openers. These pages are provided as an alternative to the Project A pages.

Investigation, Chapters 2 and 3

The Greenhouse Effect

Overview

The purpose of this Investigation is to use the mathematics in Chapters 2 and 3 to study the *greenhouse effect* and the problems of *global warming*.

Investigation (pages 68–69) Students begin the Investigation with experiments that show the effects of a light bulb on temperature at various distances. First, the students perform a control experiment that illustrates the effects of the light bulb on temperature under normal conditions. Then, the students perform an experiment that models the greenhouse effect. The plastic bag around the thermometer acts like the glass of a greenhouse or the carbon dioxide (CO_2) of Earth's atmosphere.

Working on the Investigation (page 83) Students are asked to analyze the data they gathered in the experiments.

Working on the Investigation (page 111) Students use subtraction of rational numbers to find the difference between the average temperature of Earth with CO_2 and the average temperature of Earth without CO_2 and the differences between average temperatures of planets with and without CO_2.

Working on the Investigation (page 154) Students study the change in the levels of CO_2 in the atmosphere. They write equations and make predictions.

Working on the Investigation (page 177) Students use a formula to change temperatures related to global warming from Celsius to Fahrenheit. They also change the formula to one that converts Fahrenheit to Celsius.

Closing the Investigation (page 184) Students end this Investigation by making a graph, a chart, and some equations to summarize their work. They are also asked to write a one-page letter to a group of concerned citizens about the greenhouse effect and global warming.

Mathematical Concepts

Concept	Applied In
Gather and analyze data.	Pages 68–69, 83
Use subtraction of rational numbers to find differences.	Page 111
Write equations and solve.	Page 154
Use a formula to convert temperatures.	Page 177

The Greenhouse Effect

Teacher Notes

Encourage students to be organized when working on the
Investigation. Have them keep all of their work for the Investigation
in a special location such as a separate notebook, a special section of
their notebook, or a folder that is kept in the classroom. Encourage
students to complete their work for the Investigation as they study
the related sections of Chapters 2 and 3.

To start the Investigation, gather the needed materials (lamp with
100-watt bulb, stopwatch, thermometer, and plastic zipper-style bag)
for the experiments. Distribute copies of the scoring guide so that
students will know your criteria for grading the Investigation.
Separate students into groups and give each group materials and
class time to complete the experiments. Be sure students record the
results of the experiments.

As an alternative to assigning each part of the Investigation as
it occurs in the student book, you may wish to have students
work on the Investigation for a larger period of time after completing
Chapter 3. Students may work individually or in pairs to complete
the work. In either case, encourage students to extend their work
beyond the specific items requested.

Outside Resources

Ozone Depletion, Greenhouse Gases, & Climate. National
Academy Pr., Division of National Academy of Sciences, 1989

Wilson, David A. *The Greenhouse Effect.* Lorien Hse., 1989

Scoring Guide
Chapters 2 and 3
Investigation

Level	Specific Criteria
3 Superior	• Shows thorough understanding of the concepts of *the greenhouse effect, global warming, data analysis, subtraction of rational numbers, equations,* and *formulas.* • Uses appropriate strategies to solve problems. • Computations are correct. • Written explanations are exemplary. • Charts, graph, and letter are appropriate and sensible. • Goes beyond requirements of all or some problems.
2 Satisfactory, with Minor Flaws	• Shows understanding of the concepts of *the greenhouse effect, global warming, data analysis, subtraction of rational numbers, equations,* and *formulas.* • Uses appropriate strategies to solve problems. • Computations are mostly correct. • Written explanations are effective. • Charts, graph, and letter are appropriate and sensible. • Satisfies all requirements of problems.
1 Nearly Satisfactory, with Obvious Flaws	• Shows understanding of most of the concepts of *the greenhouse effect, global warming, data analysis, subtraction of rational numbers, equations,* and *formulas.* • May not use appropriate strategies to solve problems. • Computations are mostly correct. • Written explanations are satisfactory. • Charts, graph, and letter are appropriate and sensible. • Satisfies most requirements of problems.
0 Unsatisfactory	• Shows little or no understanding of the concepts of *the greenhouse effect, global warming, data analysis, subtraction of rational numbers, equations,* and *formulas.* • Does not use appropriate strategies to solve problems. • Computations are incorrect. • Written explanations are not satisfactory. • Charts, graph, and letter are not appropriate or sensible. • Does not satisfy requirements of problems.

NAME_____ DATE _____

Investigation, Chapters 2 and 3

The Greenhouse Effect

Work with your group to add to the list of questions to be considered.

- What was the difference in the way the two experiments were designed?
- Do you think life could exist on Earth without CO_2?
- Do you think life could exist on Venus with CO_2?
- How much CO_2 was in the atmosphere in 1800 and in 1950?
- How many degrees on the Celsius scale would 15°F be?
- What is the difference between the boiling point and the freezing point on each of the scales?

_____

_____

_____

_____

_____

Reread the information about the *greenhouse effect* on pages 68–69 to find significant information. You may wish to look in some other sources. List your findings below.

_____

_____

_____

_____

Please keep this page and any other research in your Investigation folder.

Investigation, Chapters 4 and 5

Go Fish!

Overview

The purpose of this Investigation is to use the mathematics in Chapters 4 and 5 to model the *capture-recapture* method of determining the number of animals in a population.

Investigation (pages 190–191) Students begin the Investigation with an experiment that models the process used by scientists to estimate the number of fish in a large lake. Students use a lunch bag to represent the lake, beans to represent fish, and a paper cup to represent a net. They model casting a net into a lake and removing a sample of fish by scooping some beans out of the bag with a cup. Next they count and tag their sample by recording how many they caught on their first cast and replacing them with different colored beans. Then they take four more samples and record their findings each time in a chart.

Working on the Investigation (page 200) Students estimate the fish population in the lake by writing and solving proportions.

Working on the Investigation (page 227) Students find the actual population in the lake by counting all of the fish. They compare the actual population with their estimates. They also compute the percentage of tagged fish and determine the probability of catching a tagged fish.

Working on the Investigation (page 269) Students use the information in their charts to make a table, draw a mapping, and make a graph.

Working on the Investigation (page 302) Students design a different experiment that illustrates the capture-recapture method. They are also asked to compare their completed experiment with the one they completed earlier in the Investigation.

Closing the Investigation (page 314) Students end this Investigation by analyzing the strengths and weaknesses of the capture-recapture method and writing a report on how this method is used in real life. They also make a graph and draw a line of best fit to include in a speech to be given by a city council member.

Mathematical Concepts

Concept	Applied In
Gather and analyze data.	Pages 190–191
Write and solve proportions.	Page 200
Conduct and interpret probability experiments.	Page 227
Make a graph.	Page 269

Go Fish!

Teacher Notes

Encourage students to be careful when "casting" for samples and counting their "fish." Beans tend to spill easily and fall. The more accurately students count and keep track of their beans, the more effective the results.

Organization is also important in this activity. Encourage students to keep track of their beans, label their bag, and keep their data in a special location. Students should be able to easily access the data they collect as they proceed through the Investigation. Make sure that students are recording their results and storing their data properly throughout the Investigation.

To start the Investigation, gather the needed materials for each group: a cup, a paper bag, and two bags of dry beans, each a different color. Distribute copies of the scoring guide so that students will know your criteria for grading the Investigation. Give each group materials and enough class time to complete the experiments.

Students working in groups may need guidance in dividing up tasks. Suggest that they take turns "casting." Students who are not casting can help with the counting. Encourage group members to brainstorm alternative experiment designs.

As an alternative to groups, students could work on the Investigation individually or in pairs. In either case, encourage students to extend their work beyond the specific items requested.

Outside Resources

For more information, write the U.S. Fish and Wildlife Service at the following address, or visit their World Wide Web Site: http://www.fws.gov.

U.S. Fish and Wildlife Service
Department of the Interior
1849 C Street, NW
Washington, DC 20240

Buckland, S. T. *Distance Sampling: Estimating Abundance of Biological Populations.* Chapman & Hall, 1993

Scoring Guide
Chapters 4 and 5
Investigation

Level	Specific Criteria
3 Superior	• Shows thorough understanding of the concepts of *the capture-recapture method, data collection and analysis, proportions, percents,* and *probability.* • Uses appropriate strategies to solve problems. • Computations are correct. • Written explanations are exemplary. • Charts, graphs, and speech are appropriate and sensible. • Goes beyond the requirements of some or all problems.
2 Satisfactory, with Minor Flaws	• Shows understanding of the concepts of *the capture-recapture method, data collection and analysis, proportions, percents,* and *probability.* • Uses appropriate strategies to solve problems. • Computations are mostly correct. • Written explanations are effective. • Charts, graphs, and speech are appropriate and sensible. • Satisfies the requirements of problems.
1 Nearly Satisfactory, with Obvious Flaws	• Shows understanding of most of the concepts of *the capture-recapture method, data collection and analysis, proportions, percents,* and *probability.* • May not use appropriate strategies to solve problems. • Computations are mostly correct. • Written explanations are satisfactory. • Charts, graphs, and speech are appropriate and sensible. • Satisfies most requirements of problems.
0 Unsatisfactory	• Shows little or no understanding of the concepts of *the capture-recapture method, data collection and analysis, proportions, percents,* and *probability.* • Does not use appropriate strategies to solve problems. • Computations are incorrect. • Written explanations are not satisfactory. • Charts, graphs, and speech are not appropriate or sensible. • Does not satisfy the requirements of problems.

4, 5

NAME_____ DATE _____

Investigation, Chapters 4 and 5

Student Edition
Pages 190–191,
200, 227, 269, 302, 314

Go Fish!

Work with your group to add to the list of questions to be considered.

1. Find the population of fish in a pond given the following information:
   Number of fish tagged: 35
   Number of tagged fish from cast sample 1: 7
   Number of untagged fish from cast sample 2: 48
   Number of tagged fish from cast sample 2: 9
   Number of untagged fish from cast sample 2: 65

2. If you knew that 20% of a population of fish were tagged, could you determine how many total tagged fish there were? Explain how you could find that number or, if you couldn't, what else you would need to know.

   _____

   _____

3. Why is it important for scientists to keep track of animal population data?

   _____

   _____

Use this chart to record your calculations from page 227 of the Investigation.

Actual Population	
Estimated Population	
Percent in Lake Tagged	
Percent in Sample Tagged	
Probability of Catching a Tagged Fish	
Reasoning	

Use this diagram for the mapping on page 269.

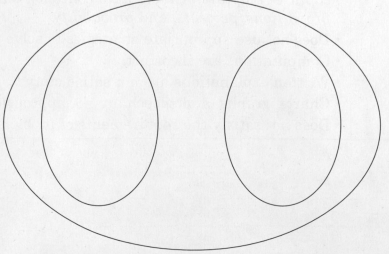

Smoke Gets In Your Eyes . . .

Overview

The purpose of this Investigation is to use the mathematics in Chapters 6 and 7 to study the effects of secondhand smoke.

Investigation (pages 320–321) Students begin the Investigation by determining the number of breaths that it takes to blow up a balloon. They determine the approximate radius of the balloon and use that data to find the volume of the spherical balloon. The volume of the balloon will allow students to estimate the volume of each breath.

Working on the Investigation (page 338) Students determine the number of cigarettes that are represented by the air in the balloon. They make two graphs—one showing the relationship between the number of breaths and the cumulative smoke in the air from smoking a cigarette, and one showing the relationship between the radius and circumference of a balloon. Students also find the volume of each balloon in milliliters.

Working on the Investigation (page 361) After collecting more data, students calculate the volume of smoke-filled air that would be produced by smoking an entire pack and then a carton of cigarettes.

Working on the Investigation (page 398) Students find the volume of smoke produced by the average smoker and the amount generated by 50 million smokers in a year. Then they estimate the number of puffs it would take to fill a room with smoke.

Working on the Investigation (page 426) Students write an equation to express the approximate number of cigarettes one would breathe if he or she worked in the smoking section of a restaurant for one year. Students relate margin of error to absolute value, write an inequality to represent how much money is spent by the average smoker in a year, and determine how much tax revenue is generated by cigarette sales in the United States.

Closing the Investigation (page 442) Students think about how they are affected by secondhand smoke and then write a paper about the health risks.

Mathematical Concepts

Concept	Applied In
Gather and analyze data.	Pages 320–321, 338
Use a formula.	Pages 320–321, 361, 398
Make a graph.	Page 338
Write equations and solve.	Page 426

NAME_____ DATE _____

6, 7

Investigation, Chapters 6 and 7 (continued)

Student Edition
Pages 320–321,
338, 361, 398, 426, 442

Smoke In Your Eyes . . .

Teacher Notes

Students will work together in groups of three. Prepare for the Investigation by gathering the necessary supplies for each group: stopwatch, grid paper, round balloons, tape measure, and string. Distribute copies of the scoring guide so that students are aware of the criteria for grading. You may want to introduce the Investigation by asking students what they know about the potential health risks associated with smoking.

Encourage groups to share responsibilities and ideas as they work together through the Investigation. It is important that students are organized and keep their work in a special place, as they will need the data they collect throughout the Investigation. Also, remind students to measure carefully and record all their results.

Allow enough time for students to complete each task. Students may need time to rest and catch their breath when they are inflating the balloons. You may also choose to do the entire Investigation over a longer period after completing Chapter 7, rather than assigning each part as it occurs in the student book. This Investigation requires group work and would not work well in groups of fewer than three students.

Outside Resources

For more information, contact the American Lung Association, 2625 Third Ave. Seattle, WA 98121-1200

Douville, Judith A. *Active and Passive Smoking Hazards in the Workplace.* VanNostrand Reinhold International Co., Ltd., 1990

Brownlee, Sharon. "The Smoke Next Door," *U.S. News & World Report.* June 20, 1994, pp. 66–68

Greisling, David and Zinn, Laura. "Where There's Secondhand Smoke. . . ," *Business Week.* August 8, 1994, pp. 43–44

Scoring Guide
Chapters 6 and 7
Investigation

Level	Specific Criteria
3 Superior	• Shows thorough understanding of the concepts of *data collection and analysis, using formulas to calculate radius and volume of a sphere, making graphs*, and *writing equations and inequalities.* • Uses appropriate strategies to solve problems. • Computations are correct. • Written explanations are exemplary. • Charts, graphs, and report are appropriate and sensible. • Goes beyond the requirements of some or all problems.
2 Satisfactory, with Minor Flaws	• Shows understanding of the concepts of *data collection and analysis, using formulas to calculate radius and volume of a sphere, making graphs*, and *writing equations and inequalities.* • Uses appropriate strategies to solve problems. • Computations are mostly correct. • Written explanations are effective. • Charts, graphs, and report are appropriate and sensible. • Satisfies the requirements of problems.
1 Nearly Satisfactory, with Obvious Flaws	• Shows understanding of most of the concepts of *data collection and analysis, using formulas to calculate radius and volume of a sphere, making graphs*, and *writing equations and inequalities.* • May not use appropriate strategies to solve problems. • Computations are mostly correct. • Written explanations are satisfactory. • Charts, graphs, and report are appropriate and sensible. • Satisfies the requirements of problems.
0 Unsatisfactory	• Shows little or no understanding of the concepts of *data collection and analysis, using formulas to calculate radius and volume of a sphere, making graphs*, and *writing equations and inequalities.* • Does not use appropriate strategies to solve problems. • Computations are incorrect. • Written explanations are not satisfactory. • Charts, graphs, and report are not appropriate or sensible. • Does not satisfy the requirements of problems.

6, 7

NAME_____ DATE _____

Investigation, Chapters 6 and 7

Student Edition
Pages 320–321,
338, 361, 398, 426, 442

Smoke Gets In Your Eyes. . .

Work with your group to answer the following questions and add others to be considered.

- If you were in a closed room with someone who smoked two packs of cigarettes (there are 20 cigarettes in a pack), what estimated volume of smoke would you breathe? How many cigarettes does that equal?

- Based on what you have found in the Investigation, would you support or oppose laws that restrict people from smoking in public buildings and enclosed spaces? Explain why you think so.

_____

_____

_____

_____

Reread the information about secondhand smoke on pages 320 and 442. Then do research to find out more about this topic. Record your findings in the chart below.

Topic	Cancer	Heart Disease	Other Respiratory Diseases
Risks to children in smokers' households			
Risks to nonsmoking adults in smokers' households			
Risks to general population encountering secondhand smoke in public places			

Investigation, Chapters 8 and 9

Ready, Set, Drop!

Overview

The purpose of this Investigation is to use the mathematics in Chapters 8 and 9 to design a hang glider.

Investigation (pages 448–449) Students begin the Investigation by using tissue paper triangles to make four models of hang gliders. They will also determine the perimeter and surface area of each triangle. Students use a stopwatch to find the drop times for each triangle. Then they examine the relationship between the drop times and the perimeter and surface area of each triangle.

Working on the Investigation (page 461) Students investigate the effect of forward motion on the hang glider models using a table top and some wire. They brainstorm methods for launching the hang glider models and then decide as a class on the best method for everyone to use. Students launch the gliders, measure the horizontal distance traveled by each glider, and write a linear equation describing each glider's path. Finally, students write a report to hypothesize what would happen if two gliders were launched at the same time from opposite sides of a cliff.

Working on the Investigation (page 519) Students determine average drop times using either mean, median, or mode, explaining their choice, and discussing appropriate situations for each method. Students draw two scatter plots that compare average glide time with perimeter and area. Then they use their scatter plots to predict the glide time and surface area for a triangle with a perimeter of 36 cm.

Working on the Investigation (page 541) Students investigate how the size of the glider and the weight of the load are related. They use their data to write a polynomial expression.

Closing the Investigation (page 548) Students organize their data to show the relationship between drop time, perimeter, and surface area; forward motion and horizontal distance; glide time, perimeter, and surface area; size of glider and average glide time; size and weight of load. The report includes an explanation of the investigation process, description of the data, analysis and conclusions from the data, hang glider recommendations for the group of people, and consideration of how the average width of a hang glider affects the group's findings.

Mathematical Concepts

Concept	Applied In
Determine perimeter and surface area.	Page 449
Write a linear equation.	Page 461
Use mean, median, or mode to determine averages.	Page 519
Draw a scatter plot.	Page 519
Write a polynomial expression.	Page 541

Ready, Set, Drop!

Teacher Notes

Have students work in groups of three. Each group will need the following supplies: construction paper, metric ruler, paper clips, scissors, stopwatch, tape, tissue paper, washers, and wire. You may want to introduce the Investigation by asking students what they know about hang gliding or bringing in pictures of hang gliders. Before beginning, distribute copies of the scoring guide so that students are aware of the criteria for grading the Investigation.

Students can share responsibilities in their groups as they complete the tasks. Encourage students to work cooperatively and brainstorm together. When the class is considering different launching methods, you may want to have a class vote to decide which to use.

Be sure that students record their results from their calculations and experiments. Also, encourage students to keep their supplies in a safe place so that they can easily retrieve their data and supplies when necessary. Students will use their data, models, charts, and supplies throughout the Investigation.

Instead of assigning each section of the Investigation as it appears in the student book, you may opt to do the Investigation as one long lesson after completing Chapter 9. Because there are a number of calculations and drop trials need to be timed, students should only work in groups for this Investigation.

Outside Resources

For more information, you can write to:

United States Hang Gliding Association
Box 66306
Los Angeles, CA 90066

Italia, Bob. *Hang Gliding*. Abdo and Daughters, 1994

Will-Harris, Tony. *Hang Gliding*. Capstone Press, 1992

Scoring Guide
Chapters 8 and 9
Investigation

Level	Specific Criteria
3 Superior	• Shows thorough understanding of the concepts of *surface area, perimeter, linear equation, polynomial expression, scatter plot, slope, best-fit line,* and *using mean, median, or mode to determine an average.* • Uses appropriate strategies to solve problems. • Computations are correct. • Written explanations are exemplary. • Charts, graphs, and report are appropriate and sensible. • Goes beyond the requirements of some or all problems.
2 Satisfactory, with Minor Flaws	• Shows understanding of the concepts of *surface area, perimeter, linear equation, polynomial expression, scatter plot, slope, best-fit line,* and *using mean, median, or mode to determine an average.* • Uses appropriate strategies to solve problems. • Computations are mostly correct. • Written explanations are effective. • Charts, graphs, and report are appropriate and sensible. • Satisfies the requirements of problems.
1 Nearly Satisfactory, with Obvious Flaws	• Shows understanding of most of the concepts of *surface area, perimeter, linear equation, polynomial expression, scatter plot, slope, best-fit line,* and *using mean, median, or mode to determine an average.* • May not use appropriate strategies to solve problems. • Computations are mostly correct. • Written explanations are satisfactory. • Charts, graphs, and report are appropriate and sensible. • Satisfies the requirements of problems.
0 Unsatisfactory	• Shows little or no understanding of the concepts of *surface area, perimeter, linear equation, polynomial expression, scatter plot, slope, best-fit line,* and *using mean, median, or mode to determine an average.* • Does not use appropriate strategies to solve problems. • Computations are incorrect. • Written explanations are not satisfactory. • Charts, graphs, and report are not appropriate or sensible. • Does not satisfy the requirements of problems.

Investigation, Chapters 8 and 9

Ready, Set, Drop!

Use this chart to record your data from Working on the Investigation, page 461.

Launch Method		
Launch Trial	Launch Height	Horizontal Distance
1		
2		
3		
4		
5		
6		
7		
8		
9		
10		
Linear Equation:		
Slope:		

Use this chart to record your data from Working on the Investigation, page 541.

Triangle	Average Glide Time
1	
2	
3	
4	

Work with your group to answer the following questions and add others to be considered.

• You have investigated the effect of forward motion on the hang gliders. Using that information, what recommendation would you make to a hang glider in regards to their starting motions?

• What predictions about glide speed would you make for a hang glider that is larger than 32 feet wide?

Investigation, Chapters 10 and 11

The Brickyard

Overview

The purpose of this Investigation is to use the mathematics from Chapters 10 and 11 to create custom-designed patios that utilize three different types of bricks.

Investigation (pages 554–555) Students begin the Investigation by reading a memo sent to the students' design team. According to the memo, the design team must create three different patio designs that utilize three different brick types. Based on specifications in the memo, students make models of each of the three bricks, explain how the dimensions relate to each other, and compare the dimensions of their models with other students.

Working on the Investigation (page 586) Students create different types of patio designs based on given specifications. They consider all possible rectangular patterns, then draw, label, and describe their process for determining the different patterns.

Working on the Investigation (page 600) Students use formulas to determine the perimeter and area of the rectangular bricks in their patterns in terms of x and y.

Working on the Investigation (page 617) Students make three graphs from the data they collected to show relationships between area, length, and width. They consider why some rectangular patterns have the same area but different perimeters.

Working on the Investigation (page 627) Students investigate possible combinations that will utilize the brick inventory at a steady rate. Students are given three possible brick combinations and must determine the dimensions, perimeters, areas, and number of patterns for each combination in terms of x and y.

Closing the Investigation (page 650) Students end this Investigation by analyzing their data and writing a report that explains their investigative process and their recommendation for possible brick patterns. The report includes sketches of possible patterns, the number of bricks used, and the dimensions, perimeter, and area expressed in terms of x and y. Students also include procedures or generalizations for finding rectangular patterns for future situations.

Mathematical Concepts

Concept	Applied In
Gather and analyze data.	Pages 617, 650
Use a formula to find perimeter and area.	Page 600
Write expressions for perimeter and area in terms of x and y.	Page 600
Make a graph.	Page 617

The Brickyard

Teacher Notes

Students will work in groups of three. Prepare for the Investigation
by gathering the necessary supplies for each group: construction
paper, scissors, and a metric ruler. Distribute copies of the scoring
guide so that students are aware of the criteria for grading. You
may want to introduce the Investigation by discussing different
brick designs around the school or bring in books that have pictures
of various brick patterns.

Encourage groups to share responsibilities and ideas as they work
together through the Investigation. It is important that students
are organized and keep their work in a special place, as they will
need the data they collect throughout the Investigation. Also,
remind students to measure carefully and record all of their results.

Allow enough time for students to complete each task. You may also
choose to do the entire Investigation over a longer period of time
after completing Chapter 11, rather than assigning each part as it
occurs in the student book. At the end of the Investigation, you may
want to display each team's favorite brick pattern in the classroom.

Other Resources

Baldwin, Edward A. *Decks and Patios: Designing and Building
Outdoor Living Spaces.* Tab Books, 1990

Meulenkamp, Wim and Andrew Plumridge. *Brickwork: Architecture
and Design.* Harry N. Abrams, Inc., Publishers, 1993

Scoring Guide
Chapters 10 and 11
Investigation

Level	Specific Criteria
3 Superior	• Shows thorough understanding of the concepts of *creating different brick pattern designs; data collection and analysis; determining the dimensions, perimeter, and area of rectangles and squares in terms of x and y;* and *making graphs.* • Uses appropriate strategies to solve problems. • Computations are correct. • Written explanations are exemplary. • Charts, graphs, and report are appropriate and sensible. • Goes beyond the requirements of some or all problems.
2 Satisfactory, with Minor Flaws	• Shows understanding of the concepts of *creating different brick pattern designs; data collection and analysis; determining the dimensions, perimeter, and area of rectangles and squares in terms of x and y;* and *making graphs.* • Uses appropriate strategies to solve problems. • Computations are mostly correct. • Written explanations are effective. • Charts, graphs, and report are appropriate and sensible. • Satisfies the requirements of problems.
1 Nearly Satisfactory, with Obvious Flaws	• Shows understanding of most of the concepts of *creating different brick pattern designs; data collection and analysis; determining the dimensions, perimeter, and area of rectangles and squares in terms of x and y;* and *making graphs.* • May not use appropriate strategies to solve problems. • Computations are mostly correct. • Written explanations are satisfactory. • Charts, graphs, and report are appropriate and sensible. • Satisfies the requirements of problems.
0 Unsatisfactory	• Shows little or no understanding of the concepts of *creating different brick pattern designs; data collection and analysis; determining the dimensions, perimeter, and area of rectangles and squares in terms of x and y;* and *making graphs.* • Does not use appropriate strategies to solve problems. • Computations are incorrect. • Written explanations are not satisfactory. • Charts, graphs, and report are not appropriate or sensible. • Does not satisfy the requirements of problems.

The Brickyard

Use this chart to record the data that you found from Working on the Investigation, page 627.

Situation 1

Dimensions			
Perimeter			
Area			

Situation 2

Dimensions			
Perimeter			
Area			

Situation 3

Dimensions			
Perimeter			
Area			

Work with your group to answer the following questions and add others to be considered.

- If you had two large square bricks, five small square bricks, and five rectangular bricks, what size rectangular patterns could you make?

- For each of the patterns that you designed, express the dimensions, perimeter, and area of each in terms of x and y.

- Which of the patterns would use up the inventory more quickly?

A Growing Concern

Overview

The purpose of this Investigation is to use the mathematics in Chapters 12 and 13 to create a landscaping plan for a family home and calculate a bid estimate of costs.

Investigation (pages 656–657) Students begin the Investigation by using their knowledge of geometry to design a rough draft of the landscaping plan. They are given the dimensions of the family home and yard and the costs for labor and materials.

Working on the Investigation (page 665) Students use graph paper to make a scale drawing of their plans and develop a detailed plan for the pool and hot tub locations. Then students calculate and justify the costs, including profit margins, for construction of the pool and hot tub. Students should keep their cost estimates with their drawings.

Working on the Investigation (page 695) Students determine and justify placement of the future play area, garden, deck and/or patio, and walkways. Then they estimate the costs for the deck and/or patio and the walkways. Have students keep their cost estimates and all of their plans together.

Working on the Investigation (page 718) Students develop a detailed plan for planting the lawn, plants, and trees for the family yard. They research the plants and trees that would be good specimens for the areas they indicated on their designs. They consider the amount of sunlight and the effects of seasonal changes, make their decisions, and explain their choices. Students then calculate the cost of materials, labor, and profit margin for planting these items and laying the sprinkler system. They must make a case for the quantity and location of the plants as well as justify the costs. Students keep all of their materials together.

Working on the Investigation (page 741) Students review their plans and make any necessary changes. They use clay, construction paper, paint, markers, and other supplies to create a 3-dimensional model of their designs. Then students use a flashlight to model the movement of the sun during the day, noting the patterns and length of time that certain areas are shaded.

Closing the Investigation (page 748) Students end the Investigation by analyzing their data and organizing a detailed financial bid. They present their proposal, scale drawing, model, and written report to classmates posing as the homeowners.

Mathematical Concepts

Concept	Applied In
Gather and analyze data.	Pages 718, 748
Use percents to determine profit margins.	Pages 665, 695, 718
Use geometry to make scale drawings.	Pages 665, 695, 718
Make a model.	Page 741

A Growing Concern

Teacher Notes

Have students work in groups of three. Prepare for the
Investigation by gathering the necessary supplies for each group:
calculator, cardboard, construction paper, flashlight, glue, markers,
modeling clay, paint, ruler, scissors, and tape. Distribute copies of
the scoring guide so that students are aware of the criteria for
grading the Investigation. You may want to introduce the
Investigation by having students discuss different landscape
designs of parks in their community.

Encourage groups to share responsibilities and ideas as they work
through the Investigation. It is important that students are
organized and keep their work in a special place, as they will need
the data they collect and their drawings throughout the
Investigation. Also, remind students to measure carefully and
record all of their measurements.

Allow enough time for students to complete each task. Groups may
need varying amounts of time to complete their models, depending
on their designs and materials. You may also choose to do the entire
Investigation over a longer period of time after completing Chapter
13, rather than assigning each part as it occurs in the student book.

Outside Resources

Reilly, Ann. *The Home Landscaper: 55 Professional Landscapes You
Can Do,* Home Planners, Inc., 1990

Turnbull, Cass. *The Complete Guide to: Landscape Design,
Renovation, and Maintenance.* Betterway Publications, Inc., 1992

Underground Sprinklers. Step-by-Step Video Instruction.
Hometime, PBS Series

Scoring Guide
Chapters 12 and 13
Investigation

Level	Specific Criteria
3 Superior	• Shows thorough understanding of the concepts of *landscaping plans, profit margins, percents, scale drawings, models, calculating dimensions,* and *using a price chart to calculate costs.* • Uses appropriate strategies to solve problems. • Computations are correct. • Written explanations are exemplary. • Drawings, model, report, and presentation are appropriate and sensible. • Goes beyond the requirements of problems.
2 Satisfactory, with Minor Flaws	• Shows understanding of the concepts of *landscaping plans, profit margins, percents, scale drawings, models, calculating dimensions,* and *using a price chart to calculate costs.* • Uses appropriate strategies to solve problems. • Computations are mostly correct. • Written explanations are effective. • Drawings, model, report, and presentation are appropriate and sensible. • Satisfies the requirements of problems.
1 Nearly Satisfactory, with Obvious Flaws	• Shows understanding of most of the concepts of *landscaping plans, profit margins, percents, scale drawings, models, calculating dimensions,* and *using a price chart to calculate costs.* • May not use appropriate strategies to solve problems. • Computations are mostly correct. • Written explanations are satisfactory. • Drawings, model, report, and presentation are appropriate and sensible. • Satisfies the requirements of problems.
0 Unsatisfactory	• Shows little or no understanding of the concepts of *landscaping plans, profit margins, percents, scale drawings, models, calculating dimensions,* and *using a price chart to calculate costs.* • Does not use appropriate strategies to solve problems. • Computations are incorrect. • Written explanations are not satisfactory. • Drawings, model, report, and presentation are not appropriate or sensible. • Does not satisfy the requirements of problems.

NAME_____ DATE _____

Investigation, Chapters 12 and 13

Student Edition Pages 656–657, 695, 718, 741, 748

A Growing Concern

Use this chart to record your calculations for the cost of materials, labor, and profit margin for each item in your plan.

Item	Cost of Materials	Labor	Profit

Work with your group to consider the following questions.

- How did the movement of the sun affect your decisions about plant choices and placement?

- If the Sanchez family was able to finance another $10,000, thus making the total amount that they can spend $75,000, what changes or additions would you make in your plan?

- List the elements that your group proposed to include for an effective sales presentation.

Chapter 1 Project A

1

The "Write" Way

1. Conduct a survey in which you ask at least 20 working people to rank the importance of good writing skills from 1 to 3, with 1 being "very important for my job," 2 being "somewhat important for my job," and 3 being "not important for my job."

2. Using the data you gathered in step 1, calculate the percentage of responses in each category.

3. Go to the library and find a book that contains descriptions of various jobs and the skills that are necessary to do them. Make a list of jobs that require good writing skills.

4. Research the kind of writing that is involved in each career on your list. You might want to interview people who do a lot of writing on the job. Find out about the purpose of the writing each person does. Is it meant to inform? To entertain? To persuade? You might also want to ask about the audience for each piece of writing.

5. Make a poster or brochure that helps younger students understand the importance of having strong writing skills.

To: The Parents of _____

The "Write" Way

Your student is about to start Chapter 1 in Algebra 1. In this chapter, your student will be studying mathematical expressions and properties. During the study of this chapter, your student will be working on a project about the importance of good writing skills for various jobs. The following is a list of activities your student must complete for this project.

1. Conduct a survey in which he or she asks at least 20 working people to rank the importance of good writing skills for their jobs from 1 to 3, with 1 being "very important for my job," 2 being "somewhat important for my job," and 3 being "not important for my job."

2. Use the data gathered in step 1 to calculate the percentage of responses in each category.

3. Go to the library and find a book that contains descriptions of various jobs and the skills that are necessary to do them. Make a list of jobs that require good writing skills.

4. Research the kind of writing that is involved in each career on his or her list. He or she might want to interview people who do a lot of writing on the job. Your student should find out about the purpose of the writing each person does. Is it meant to inform? To entertain? To persuade? He or she might also want to ask about the audience for each piece of writing.

5. Make a poster or brochure that helps younger students understand the importance of having strong writing skills.

Your student's project is due on _____ .

Please sign and return the bottom portion by _____ .

I have read the requirements for this project and have discussed them with my student.

Parent's Signature _____

Student's Name _____

Class Period _____

1

Chapter 1 Project B

Statistically Speaking

1. Research the number of games each team in major league baseball has won so far this season. You should be able to find this information in the sports section of a daily newspaper.

2. Use the data you gathered in exercise 1 to make a back-to-back stem-and-leaf plot of the wins in the National League and the American League.

3. Using the completed stem-and-leaf plot, compare the records of National League and American League teams. Is one team much better than all of the others? Is one team much worse than all of the others?

4. Select the team that you consider to be either the best or worst in major league baseball. Find (or compute) the team's winning percentage.

5. Record the outcomes of the team's next five games. Sketch a reasonable graph showing how the team's winning percentage changed during this five-game period.

6. Write a newspaper article about the best or worst team in major league baseball. Include the graph from exercise 5 and note any trends you see.

To: The Parents of _____

Statistically Speaking

Your student is about to start Chapter 1 in Algebra 1. In this chapter, your student will be studying mathematical expressions and properties, as well as learning how to represent data graphically. During the study of this chapter, your student will be working on a project involving sports statistics. The following is a list of activities your student must complete for this project.

1. Research the number of games each team in major league baseball has won so far this season. He or she should be able to find this information in the sports section of a daily newspaper.

2. Use the data he or she gathered in exercise 1 to make a back-to-back stem-and-leaf plot of the wins in the National League and the American League.

3. Use the completed stem-and-leaf plot to compare the records of National League and American League teams. Determine if one team is much better or much worse than all of the others.

4. Select the best or worst team in major league baseball. Find (or compute) the team's winning percentage.

5. Record the outcome of the team's next five games. Sketch a reasonable graph showing how the team's winning percentage changed during this five-game period.

6. Write a newspaper article about the best or worst team in major league baseball. Include the graph from exercise 5 and note any trends.

Your student's project is due on _____ .

Please sign and return the bottom portion by _____ .

I have read the requirements for this project and have discussed them with my student.

Parent's Signature _____

Student's Name _____

Class Period _____

Chapter 2 Project A

Good for You!

1. Choose at least five different kinds of breakfast cereal. Copy the information given in the "Nutrition Facts" chart on each package and note the price. (Be sure each package contains the same amount of cereal.)

2. For each cereal find the total number of vitamins with a Percent Daily Value of at least 25% in one serving. (Use the information given for the cereal alone—without milk.)

3. Rank the cereals in order from least sugar to most sugar per serving.

4. Rank the cereals in order from lowest price to highest price.

5. Present your findings to the class by doing one of the following activities.

   • Make a poster that summarizes what you discovered about the cereals.

   • Write an article for the school newspaper about nutrition in breakfast cereals.

   • Create a magazine or television ad for the cereal you think is most nutritious.

Chapter 2 Project A

To: The Parents of _____

Good for You!

Your student is about to start Chapter 2 of Algebra 1. In this chapter, your student will be locating integers on a number line, adding and subtracting integers and rational numbers, multiplying and dividing integers and rational numbers, identifying rational and irrational numbers, and estimating square roots. During the study of this chapter, your student will be working on a project about the nutritional value of different breakfast cereals. The following is a list of activities your student must complete for this project.

1. Your student will choose at least five different kinds of breakfast cereal. He or she will copy the information given in the "Nutrition Facts" chart on each package and note the price.

2. For each cereal, your student will find the total number of vitamins with a Percent Daily Value of at least 25% in one serving. (He or she will use the information given for the cereal alone—without milk.)

3. Your student will rank the cereals in order from least sugar to most sugar per serving.

4. Your student will rank the cereals in order from lowest price to highest price.

5. Your student will choose one of the following activities to present his or her findings to the class.
   • Make a poster that summarizes what he or she discovered about the cereals.
   • Write an article for the school newspaper about nutrition in breakfast cereals.
   • Create a magazine or television ad for the cereal he or she thinks is most nutritious.

Your student's project is due on _____.

Please sign and return the bottom portion by _____.

I have read the requirements for this project and have discussed them with my student.

Parent's Signature _____

Student's Name _____

Class Period _____

Game Time

Materials: cardboard; markers; number cubes, spinners, or index cards

1. Work with a partner. Brainstorm ideas for a new board game. The board itself must include a starting point and a finish point and squares in between. The theme for the game can be anything you find interesting. (Possibilities include intergalactic travel, a mysterious labyrinth, a treasure hunt, or a bicycle race.)

2. Decide how players will move their game pieces along the board. You may use two number cubes, two spinners, or integers written on index cards to indicate the distance a game piece will be moved. Use positive and negative integers.

3. Include a square on which you have written "−1." Whenever a player lands on this square, he or she must multiply the number of squares he or she just moved by −1 and move again.

4. Create several different game pieces or collect game pieces from existing games.

5. Write a complete set of directions for your game. Play the game once to see if it has any "bugs" that you want to fix.

6. Play the final version of your game and/or games created by your classmates at a time designated by the teacher.

Chapter 2 Project B

To: The Parents of _____

Game Time

Your student is about to start Chapter 2 of Algebra 1. In this chapter, your student will be locating integers on a number line, adding and subtracting integers and rational numbers, multiplying and dividing integers and rational numbers, identifying rational and irrational numbers, and estimating square roots. During the study of this chapter, your student will be working with a partner on a project involving the creation of a board game that uses positive and negative integers. The following is a list of activities your student must complete for this project.

1. With a partner, your student will brainstorm ideas for a new board game. The board itself must include a starting point and a finish point and squares in between. The theme can be anything your student and his or her partner find interesting. (Possibilities include intergalactic travel, a mysterious labyrinth, a treasure hunt, or a bicycle race.)

2. The pair will decide how players will move their game pieces along the board. Players will use two number cubes, two spinners, or integers written on index cards to indicate the distance a game piece will be moved. They will use positive and negative integers.

3. The pair will include a square on which "−1" has been written. Whenever a player lands on this square, he or she must multiply the number of squares he or she just moved by −1 and move again.

4. The pair will create several different game pieces or collect game pieces from existing games.

5. The pair will write a complete set of directions for the game. They will play the game once to see if it has any "bugs" and make any necessary corrections.

6. The pair will play the final version of the game and/or games created by other students at a time designated by the teacher.

Your student's project is due on _____ .

Please sign and return the bottom portion by _____ .

I have read the requirements for this project and have discussed them with my student.

Parent's Signature _____

Student's Name _____

Class Period _____

3

Chapter 3 Project A

Higher Learning

1. What do you think the ideal college would be like? Would it be large or small? Would it be located in a big city or a small town? Would the weather be warm or cold? What would the professors, classes, and sports teams be like? Think about your answers to these questions. Make up your own questions. Then write a description of your ideal college.

2. Go to the library and find a book with descriptions of colleges. Make a list of schools that fit the description that you wrote for exercise 1.

3. Find the estimated annual cost of attending each school.

4. Research the financial aid that is available to students attending three of the schools on your list. What scholarships do the colleges offer? Will the schools assist you in finding a part-time job? How much money can you earn on such a job? Can you get a loan from the colleges, the federal government, or some other agency?

5. Draw up a financial plan for meeting your college expenses.

6. Work with a partner to complete one of the projects listed below, based on the information you gathered in exercises 1–5.

   - Conduct an interview.
   - Write a book report.
   - Write a proposal.
   - Write an article for the school paper.
   - Stage a debate.
   - Write a report.
   - Make a display.
   - Make a graph or chart.
   - Plan an activity.
   - Design a checklist.

To: The Parents of _____

Higher Learning

Your student is about to start Chapter 3 in Algebra 1. In this chapter, your student will be studying algebraic equations and measures of central tendency. During the study of this chapter, your student will be working on a project about financial planning for college. The following is a list of activities your student must complete for this project.

1. Describe his or her ideal college. Your student will consider such factors as size, location, weather, academic credentials, sports teams, and any other factors they think are important.

2. Go to the library and find a book with descriptions of colleges. Make a list of schools that fit his or her description of the ideal college.

3. Find the estimated annual cost of attending each school.

4. Research the financial aid that is available to students attending three of the schools on his or her list. What scholarships do the colleges offer? Will the schools assist students in finding a part-time job? How much money can students earn on such a job? Can students get a loan from the colleges, the federal government, or some other agency?

5. Draw up a financial plan for meeting his or her college expenses.

6. Work with a partner to complete one of the projects listed below, based on the information he or she gathered in exercises 1–5 above.

   - Conduct an interview.
   - Write a book report.
   - Write a proposal.
   - Write an article for the school paper.
   - Stage a debate.

   - Write a report.
   - Make a display.
   - Make a graph or chart.
   - Plan an activity.
   - Design a checklist.

Your student's project is due on _____ .

Please sign and return the bottom portion by _____ .

I have read the requirements for this project and have discussed them with my student.

Parent's Signature _____

Student's Name _____

Class Period _____

Chapter 3 Project B

Numbering Systems

Materials   posterboard
markers

1. Throughout history, various civilizations have used different
   systems of numeration. Research an early numbering system
   from the list below.

    African
    Arabic
    Armenian
    Babylonian
    Chinese
    Egyptian
    Gothic
    Greek
    Hindu/Brahmi
    Incan
    Mayan
    Old English
    Roman
    Runes
    Sanskrit
    Thai
    Tibetan

2. Draw a complete set of numbers in your selected system on
   posterboard.

3. Develop simple addition and subtraction problems in your
   selected system.

4. Make a presentation to the class. Be sure to prepare some
   practice problems for the class to do after your presentation.

Chapter 3 Project B

To: The Parents of _____

Numbering Systems

Your student is about to start Chapter 3 in Algebra 1. In this chapter, your student will be studying algebraic equations and measures of central tendency. During the study of this chapter, your student will be working on a project about numbering systems. The following is a list of activities your student must complete for this project.

1. Go to the library and research an early numbering system from the list below.

African	Incan
Arabic	Mayan
Armenian	Old English
Babylonian	Roman
Chinese	Runes
Egyptian	Sanskrit
Gothic	Thai
Greek	Tibetan
Hindu/Brahmi	

2. Draw a complete set of numbers in his or her selected system on posterboard.

3. Develop simple addition and subtraction problems in his or her selected system.

4. Make a presentation to the class. Be sure he or she prepares some practice problems for the class to do after his or her presentation.

Your student's project is due on _____ .

Please sign and return the bottom portion by _____ .

I have read the requirements for this project and have discussed them with my student.

Parent's Signature _____

Student's Name _____

Class Period _____

Chapter 4 Project A

A World of Names

1. For this project, you will work in a small group to research names and naming customs of different ethnic groups. In some groups, for example, the family name comes before the other names. Sometimes, a person's full family name is made up of both parents' names. Use reference books to find out more about such customs. You can also ask friends from different ethnic backgrounds about customs connected with their names. Find out what some common family names mean.

2. Do research to find out the most common family names of students at your school. You may be able to obtain lists of students' last names from classroom teachers or from the principal's office.

3. Make a list of the five most common names at your school. Determine what percent of the students at your school has each of these names.

4. Do research to find out the most common family names in your community. Use one or more telephone directories and the list of the most common family names at your school. Make a list of the five most common family names in your community and determine what percent of the population has each name.

5. If possible, interview an expert in the field of demographics, the study of human populations. Ask how the results of your research would have been different 25, 50, and 100 years ago. Also, ask the interviewee what a list of common last names might look like 100 years from now.

6. Write an article for your school newspaper about names and naming customs and the results of your investigation.

To: The Parents of _____

A World of Names

Your student is about to start Chapter 4 in Algebra 1. In this chapter your student will be using proportional reasoning. He or she will be solving proportions, using trigonometric ratios, solving percent problems, and working with probability. During the study of this chapter your student will be working on a project about family names. The following is a list of activities your student must complete for this project.

1. For this project, your student will work in a small group to research names and naming customs of different ethnic groups. In some groups, for example, the family name comes before the other names. Sometimes, a person's full family name is made up of both parents' names. Your student will use reference books to find out more about such customs. He or she can also ask friends from different ethnic backgrounds about customs connected with their names and what some common family names mean.

2. Your student will do research to find out the most common family names of students at school. He or she may be able to obtain lists of students' last names from classroom teachers or from the principal's office.

3. Your student will make a list of the five most common names at school and determine what percent of the students at the school has each of these names.

4. Your student will do research to find out the most common family names in your community. He or she will use one or more telephone directories and the list of the most common family names at school. He or she will make a list of the five most common family names in your community and determine what percent of the population has each name.

5. If possible, your student will interview an expert in the field of demographics, the study of human populations. He or she will ask how the results of his or her research would have been different 25, 50, and 100 years ago and what a list of common last names might look like 100 years from now.

6. With his or her group, your student will write an article for the school newspaper about names and naming customs and the results of the investigation.

Your student's project is due on _____ .

Please sign and return the bottom portion by _____ .

I have read the requirements for this project and have discussed them with my student.

Parent's Signature _____

Student's Name _____

Class Period _____

Such a Deal

1. Work in a small group. Collect newspapers and catalogs that advertise discounted prices on different products or services. Be sure the advertisements you collect represent a wide variety of methods for computing discounted prices. For example, you may find a one-third-off sale, a 25% discount, and a $50 rebate on the same product.

2. Choose one of the products or services from the ads you collected in exercise 1. Be sure to choose a product that is advertised by several different suppliers with a variety of discounts. Compare the discounts by answering the questions below.

   a. Which supplier offers the lowest price?

   b. Which supplier offers the best product or extent of service?

3. Select the best product or service and the best supplier. (Remember that the best choice may not necessarily be the one with the lowest price!)

4. Decide how you want to present your findings to the class. Possibilities include writing a newspaper article or recording a report for a radio or television newscast.

Chapter 4 Project B

To: The Parents of _____

Such a Deal

Your student is about to start Chapter 4 in Algebra 1. In this chapter, your student will be studying percents and proportional reasoning. During the study of this chapter, your student will be working on a project about sales and discounts. The following is a list of activities your student must complete for this project.

1. Your student will work in a small group. He or she will collect newspapers and catalogs that advertise discounted prices on different products or services. Your student should be sure the advertisements he or she collects represent a wide variety of methods for computing discounted prices. For example, your student may find a one-third-off sale, a 25% discount, and a $50 rebate on the same product.

2. Group members will choose one of the products or services from the ads collected in exercise 1. Group members should choose a product that is advertised by several different suppliers with a variety of discounts. Your student will compare the discounts by answering the questions below.

   a. Which supplier offers the lowest price?

   b. Which supplier offers the best product or extent of service?

3. Your student's group will select the best product or service and the best supplier. (Your student should remember that the best choice may not necessarily be the one with the lowest price!)

4. Your student's group will decide how to present its findings to the class. Possibilities include writing a newspaper article or recording a report for a radio or television newscast.

Your student's project is due on _____ .

Please sign and return the bottom portion by _____ .

I have read the requirements for this project and have discussed them with my student.

Parent's Signature _____

Student's Name _____

Class Period _____

5 Chapter 5 Project A

Venues and Revenues

1. Work with a partner to make a list of places in your area that feature live performances by musicians. You may need to look in a newspaper for ideas.

2. Do research to find out the seating capacity of each place, or venue, you listed in exercise 1. Also, find out what kind(s) of music is (are) usually performed in each venue. Present your findings in the form of a graph.

3. Write an equation that can be used to estimate the amount of money that would be generated by a sold-out show at each venue.

4. Find the average ticket price for upcoming concerts at the venues you researched. You may be able to do this by looking at newspaper ads.

5. Use the information about ticket prices from exercise 4 and the equation from exercise 3 to determine how much money different concerts would make at each venue. Then find out how the money from ticket sales is divided among a venue's owners, the musicians, the promoter, the company selling the tickets, and others.

6. Use what you've learned to write a newspaper article about the business of performing live music. Be sure to include any graphs you've drawn.

Chapter 5 Project A

To: The Parents of _____

Venues and Revenues

Your student is about to start Chapter 5 in Algebra 1. In this chapter, your student will be studying functions and graphs. During the study of this chapter, your student will be working on a project on the business of performing live music. The following is a list of activities your student must complete for this project.

1. Work with a partner to make a list of places in your area that feature live performances by musicians. Your student may need to look in a newspaper for ideas.

2. Do research to find out the seating capacity of each place, or venue, he or she listed in exercise 1. Also, find out what kind(s) of music is (are) usually performed in each venue. Present his or her findings in the form of a graph.

3. Write an equation that can be used to estimate the amount of money that would be generated by a sold-out show at each venue.

4. Find the average ticket price for upcoming concerts at the venues he or she researched. Your student may be able to do this by looking at newspaper ads.

5. Use the information about ticket prices from exercise 4 and the equation from exercise 3 to determine how much money different concerts would make at each venue. Then find out how the money from ticket sales is divided among a venue's owners, the musicians, the promoter, the company selling the tickets, and others.

6. Use what he or she has learned to write a newspaper article about the business of performing live music. Your student should be sure to include any graphs he or she has drawn.

Your student's project is due on _____ .

Please sign and return the bottom portion by _____ .

I have read the requirements for this project and have discussed them with my student.

Parent's Signature _____

Student's Name _____

Class Period _____

5

Chapter 5 Project B

Raising Funds

1. Members of organizations such as sports teams or clubs often need to raise money. To do this, they may decide to sell things like candy bars or wrapping paper, or they may decide to hold a car wash or a garage sale. If you are a member of an organization, make a list of items for which your group needs money. If you are not a member of an organization, choose a group and make a list of items for which they might need money.

2. Do research to find the cost of the items in the list you made in exercise 1. Choose the items you want to raise money to buy.

3. Plan a fund-raiser to make the money for the items you chose in exercise 2. As you complete your plans, think about the costs involved in conducting the fund-raiser and how much you plan to charge. Include equations that describe your plans and show how many customers or items you will need to make the necessary profit for your purchase.

4. Present your ideas for your fund-raiser to your organization or class. Make a poster that describes your event and communicates your ideas. Be sure to include the equations you wrote in exercise 3 in your presentation.

To: The Parents of _____

Raising Funds

Your student is about to start Chapter 5 in Algebra 1. In this chapter, your student will be studying functions and graphs. During the study of this chapter, your student will be working on a project about fund-raisers. The following is a list of activities your student must complete for this project.

1. Members of organizations such as sports teams or clubs often need to raise money. To do this, they may decide to sell things like candy bars or wrapping paper, or they may decide to hold a car wash or garage sale. If your student is a member of such an organization, he or she will make a list of items for which his or her group needs money. If your student is not a member of such an organization, he or she will choose a group and make a list of items for which they might need money.

2. Your student will do research to find the cost of the items in the list he or she made in exercise 1. Your student will choose the items he or she wants to raise money to buy.

3. Your student will plan a fund-raiser to make the money for the items he or she chose in exercise 2. As your student completes his or her plans, he or she should think about the costs involved in conducting the fund-raiser and how much he or she plans to charge. Your student's work should include equations that describe his or her plans and show how many customers or items he or she will need to make the necessary profit for his or her purchase.

4. Your student will present his or her ideas for the fund-raiser to the class. Your student will make a poster that describes his or her event and communicates his or her ideas. Your student should be sure to use the equations he or she wrote in exercise 3 in his or her presentation.

Your student's project is due on _____ .

Please sign and return the bottom portion by _____ .

I have read the requirements for this project and have discussed them with my student.

Parent's Signature _____

Student's Name _____

Class Period _____

Analyzing Immigration

1. Today, many people consider illegal immigration a significant problem for our nation. For this project you will work in a small group to research illegal immigration to the United States. Use reference works to find out more about this subject, including answers to the following questions.

   • How many illegal immigrants are estimated to live in the United States at this time?

   • How many people have entered the United States illegally in each of the last ten years?

   • What draws people to the United States and why are many willing to enter illegally?

   • What do politicians and public figures cite as positive and negative effects of illegal immigration?

2. Research immigration laws in the United States, particularly recent ones. What effects have these laws had on the number of persons entering the United States illegally?

3. Decide whether your group would be in favor of or opposed to spending large amounts of government money on keeping illegal immigrants out of the United States. Prepare an oral presentation of your group's position, in which each group member will participate. Use a scatter plot to show whether the correlation between the number of illegal immigrants and some other variable, such as a state's spending on welfare, prisons, or schools, is strong or weak.

4. Pair up with a group that takes the position opposite to your own and make your presentations to the rest of the class.

To: The Parents of _____

Analyzing Immigration

Your student is about to start Chapter 6 in Algebra 1. In this chapter your student will be analyzing linear equations. He or she will explore finding the slope of lines, writing linear equations, drawing scatter plots, and graphing linear equations. During the study of this chapter your student will be working on a project about immigration. The following is a list of activities your student must complete for this project.

1. Today, many people consider illegal immigration a significant problem for our nation. In this project your student will work in a small group to research illegal immigration to the United States. Your student will use reference works to find out more about this subject, including answers to the following questions.

   - How many illegal immigrants are estimated to live in the United States at this time?
   - How many people have entered the United States illegally in each of the last ten years?
   - What draws people to the United States and why are many willing to enter illegally?
   - What do politicians and public figures cite as positive and negative effects of illegal immigration?

2. Your student and his or her group will research immigration laws in the United States, particularly recent ones. They will try to find out what effects these laws have had on the number of persons entering the United States illegally.

3. Your student's group will decide whether it would be in favor of or opposed to spending large amounts of government money on keeping illegal immigrants out of the United States. The group will prepare an oral presentation of its position, in which each group member will participate. The group will use a scatter plot to show whether the correlation between the number of illegal immigrants and some other variable, such as a state's spending on welfare, prisons, or schools, is strong or weak.

4. Your student's group will pair up with a group that takes the position opposite to its own. The two groups will make their presentations to the rest of the class.

Your student's project is due on _____ .

Please sign and return the bottom portion by _____ .

I have read the requirements for this project and have discussed them with my student.

Parent's Signature _____

Student's Name _____

Class Period _____

Growing Graphs

1. Work in a small group. Do research to find out about several
   different rapidly growing plants that can be grown easily from
   seeds. Decide with your group which plant you would like to
   grow.

2. Plant several seeds for your chosen plant in three different pots.
   Put each pot under different growing conditions. For example,
   you might want to put one pot in bright light, one in medium
   light, and one in low light and/or add varying amounts of
   fertilizer to the pots.

3. As your plants begin to grow, measure the height of the tallest
   plant in each pot. Record the height each day. Continue to
   record the data until there is a significant difference in the
   heights of the plants in the different pots.

4. Use a different colored pencil to draw a graph of the data for
   each pot. Draw a line of best fit for each graph. Write the point-
   slope form of an equation for each line. Describe the differences
   among the graphs. Explain how the slope of each line shows the
   differences in the growth of the plants in the different pots.

5. Draw one graph that combines the individual graphs you drew
   in exercise 4. Draw each line in the same color you used in
   exercise 4. Compare the graphs. Record any observations that
   you did not notice by studying the individual graphs.

6. Write a report to summarize your findings. Be sure to include
   the graphs you drew in exercises 4 and 5. Share your report
   with the class.

Chapter 6 Project B

To: The Parents of _____

Growing Graphs

Your student is about to start Chapter 6 in Algebra 1. In this chapter, your student will be studying linear equations. During the study of this chapter, your student will be working on a project about the growth of seeds. The following is a list of activities your student must complete for this project.

1. Your student will work in a small group. Your student's group will do research to find out about several different rapidly growing plants that can be grown easily from seeds. Your student will decide with his or her group which plant to grow.

2. Your student will plant several seeds for his or her chosen plant in three different pots. Your student will put each pot under different growing conditions. For example, your student might vary the amounts of sunlight and/or fertilizer the pots receive.

3. As your student's plants begin to grow, your student will measure the height of the tallest plant in each pot. Your student will record the height each day. He or she will continue to record the data until there is a significant difference in the heights of the plants in the different pots.

4. Your student will use a different colored pencil to draw a graph of the data for each pot and will draw a line of best fit for each graph. He or she will write the point-slope form of an equation for each line and will describe the differences among the graphs. Your student will also explain how the slope of each line shows the differences in the growth of the plants in the different pots.

5. Your student will draw one graph that combines the individual graphs he or she drew in exercise 4. Your student will draw each line in the same color he or she used in exercise 4. Your student will then compare the graphs. Your student will record any observations that he or she did not notice by studying the individual graphs.

6. Your student will write a report to summarize his or her findings. Your student should be sure to include the graphs he or she drew in exercises 4 and 5. Your student will share his or her report with the class.

Your student's project is due on _____ .

Please sign and return the bottom portion by _____ .

I have read the requirements for this project and have discussed them with my student.

Parent's Signature _____

Student's Name _____ .

Class Period _____

Algebra 1

7 Chapter 7 Project A

Choose a Career

1. What career do you want to pursue after you graduate from high school? You may be considering several different careers; if so, which of these are you most likely to choose? Do research to find out more about this career. Are there any courses you can take in high school that will help you prepare for your career?

2. What are the requirements for entering your chosen field? Do research to find out about where you can get the necessary education and/or training. Be sure to find out about the money and time you will need to invest to receive such education and/or training.

3. Think about how you will pay for your education and/or training. Write a plan for saving the money required. Consider the answers to the following questions as you work on your savings plan.

   • Can you start saving money now?
   • Are your parents or guardians saving money for you?
   • Are there scholarships for which you might be eligible?

   Write an inequality that expresses the minimum amount you plan to save from all possible sources.

4. Share your plan with your classmates. Ask them if they think the plan is realistic and if they can offer any suggestions for improving it.

Chapter 7 Project A

To: The Parents of _____

Choose a Career

Your student is about to start Chapter 7 in Algebra 1. In this chapter, your student will be studying linear inequalities. During the study of this chapter, your student will be working on a project about the costs associated with beginning a career. The following is a list of activities your student must complete for this project.

1. Your student will decide what career he or she wants to pursue after he or she graduates from high school. Your student will do research to find out more about this career, including what courses, if any, can be taken in high school to help him or her prepare for this career.

2. Your student will do research to find out where he or she can get the necessary education and/or training to enter his or her chosen field and how much money and time will need to be invested.

3. Your student will think about financing his or her education and/or training. Your student will write out a plan for saving the money required. Your student should consider the answers to the following questions as he or she works on the savings plan.

   • Can he or she start saving money now?
   • Are you, the parents or guardians, saving money for him or her?
   • Are there scholarships for which he or she might be eligible?

   Your student will write an inequality that expresses the minimum amount he or she plans to save from all possible sources.

4. Your student will share his or her plan with the rest of the class. Other students will comment on the plan and suggest improvements.

Your student's project is due on _____ .

Please sign and return the bottom portion by _____ .

I have read the requirements for this project and have discussed them with my student.

Parent's Signature _____

Student's Name _____

Class Period _____

Chapter 7 Project B

Healthy Ranges

1. In this project, you are going to discover how the range of heights, heart rates, and body temperatures among you and some of your classmates compares with the range that is typical for all people your age. Begin by doing research to find out what these three measurements mean and what the typical ranges are for people your age.

2. Work in a group of three. Decide with your group how you are going to take these measurements. If possible, set up a room with three stations. Decide which station each member of your group will run. Work with your group to set up a way of keeping track of the data gathered from each station.

3. Conduct a trial run of your stations with members of your group. After the trial run is completed, discuss any changes that you may need to make before you begin to collect more data.

4. Ask at least 20 classmates to participate in your project. Have each participant visit each station and have group members collect the necessary data.

5. Work with your group to analyze the data you have collected. Write inequalities that describe the range of each set of measurements. Draw several different graphs to describe each set of data and its range. Make posters containing the graphs.

6. Present your findings to the class. Use the posters to help your classmates visualize the results. Be sure to compare your results with the typical range of measurements for people your age.

To: The Parents of _____

Healthy Ranges

Your student is about to start Chapter 7 in Algebra 1. In this chapter, your student will be studying linear inequalities. During the study of this chapter, your student will be working on a project in which height, heart rate, and body temperature data are collected and analyzed. The following is a list of activities your student must complete for this project.

1. In this project, your student is going to discover how the range of heights, heart rates, and body temperatures among some of his or her classmates compares with the range that is typical for people their age. Your student will begin by doing research to find out what these three measurements mean and what the typical ranges are for the people his or her age.

2. Your student will work in a group of three. The group will decide how group members are going to take these measurements. If possible, they will set up a room with three stations. The group will decide which station each group member will run and set up a way of keeping track of the data gathered from each station.

3. Your student's group will conduct a trial run of the stations using the members of the group. After the trial run is completed, they will discuss any changes that the group may need to make before beginning to collect more data.

4. Your student's group will ask at least 20 classmates to participate in the project. Each participant will visit each station while your student's group collects the necessary data.

5. Your student's group will analyze the data that have been collected. The group will write inequalities that describe the range of each set of measurements. The group will draw several different graphs to describe each set of data and its range. The group will make posters containing the graphs.

6. Your student will present his or her findings to the class, using the posters from exercise 5 to help his or her classmates visualize the results. Your student should be sure to compare his or her results with the typical range of measurements for people his or her age.

Your student's project is due on _____ .

Please sign and return the bottom portion by _____ .

I have read the requirements for this project and have discussed them with my student.

Parent's Signature _____

Student's Name _____

Class Period _____

8

Chapter 8 Project A

Games People Play

1. Work with a partner. Select 50–100 people over the age of 7 in your neighborhood or family for a survey.

2. Ask the people you have selected to name any sports they have participated in at least once during the last year. (People who name swimming, exercise walking, exercising with equipment, running/jogging, or aerobics can be counted only if they have done one of these particular activities at least 6 times during the year.)

3. Determine the number of people who participated in each sport. What percent of the people you surveyed participated in each sport?

4. List the sports in order from greatest to least participation.

5. Compare your results with the table in the chapter opener. Are your results similar? If not, how do the results differ? Are you surprised at the results? Explain.

6. Complete one of the following activities based on your data:

   • Put your data together with that of another group or two. Find the percent of participation for each sport and make a new list of sports, ranked from greatest to least participation. Share your findings with the class by making a poster or giving an oral report.

   • Write an article for the school newspaper.

   • Make a pictograph for the school newspaper.

   • Do some library research and discover the participation in sports of past generations. What sporting pastimes were the most popular in 1850? 1900? 1950? What do you think will be the most popular sports in 2000? Write a report or make an oral presentation of your findings.

Chapter 8 Project A

To: The Parents of _____

Games People Play

Your student is about to start Chapter 8 in Algebra 1. In this chapter, your student will be solving systems of equations, solving problems by organizing data, and solving systems of inequalities. During the study of this chapter, your student will be working on a project about participation in different sports. The following is a list of activities your student must complete for this project.

1. Work with a partner. Select 50–100 people over the age of 7 in his or her neighborhood or family for a survey.
2. Ask the people he or she has selected to name any sports they have participated in at least once during the last year. (People who name swimming, exercise walking, exercising with equipment, running/jogging, or aerobics can be counted only if they have done one of these particular activities at least 6 times during the year.)
3. Determine the number of people who participated in each sport. What percent of the people he or she surveyed participated in each sport?
4. List the sports in order from greatest to least participation.
5. Compare his or her results with the table in the chapter opener. Are his or her results similar? If not, how do the results differ? Is he or she surprised at the results? Explain.
6. Complete one of the following activities based on his or her data:

   • Put his or her data together with that of another group or two. Find the percent of participation for each sport and make a new list of sports, ranked from greatest to least participation. Share his or her findings with the class by making a poster or giving an oral report.
   • Write an article for the school newspaper.
   • Make a pictograph for the school newspaper.
   • Do some library research and discover the participation in sports of past generations. What sporting pastimes were the most popular in 1850? 1900? 1950? What does he or she think will be the most popular sports in 2000? Write a report or make an oral presentation of his or her findings.

Your student's project is due on _____ .

Please sign and return the bottom portion by _____ .

I have read the requirements for this project and have discussed them with my student.

Parent's Signature _____

Student's Name _____

Class Period _____

Chapter 8 Project B

Linear Thinking

1. Go to the library and find out what you can about an application of solving systems of inequalities called linear programming. This technique has been used since World War II to solve a wide variety of problems in business, industry, and government. Encyclopedia articles or reference books might be helpful, as well as books on applied mathematics.

2. Read some of the examples to understand how linear programming works.

3. Interview some people in your community who you think may use linear programming. You might try contacting someone who works at a school bus company, factory, transportation department, environmental/conservation agency, public energy company, or local telephone company. Ask each person to give you a simple example of how this technique helps them do their jobs.

4. Use one of the examples you have researched or make up a problem that can be solved using linear programming.

5. Make a presentation of your problem and its solution to your class. Include a large graph that demonstrates how the technique works.

Chapter 8 Project B

To: The Parents of _____

Linear Thinking

Your student is about to start Chapter 8 in Algebra 1. In this chapter, your student will be solving systems of equations, solving problems by organizing data, and solving systems of inequalities. During the study of this chapter, your student will be working on a project about linear programming. The following is a list of activities your student must complete for this project.

1. Go to the library and find out what he or she can about an application of solving systems of inequalities called linear programming. This technique has been used since World War II to solve a wide variety of problems in business, industry, and government. Encyclopedia articles or reference books might be helpful, as well as books on applied mathematics.

2. Read some of the examples to understand how linear programming works.

3. Interview some people in his or her community who he or she thinks may use linear programming. He or she might try contacting someone who works at a school bus company, factory, transportation department, environmental/conservation agency, public energy company, or local telephone company. Ask each person to give him or her a simple example of how this technique helps them do their jobs.

4. Use one of the examples he or she has researched or make up a problem that can be solved using linear programming.

5. Make a presentation of his or her problem and its solution to his or her class. Include a large graph that demonstrates how the technique works.

Your student's project is due on _____ .

- -

Please sign and return the bottom portion by _____ .

I have read the requirements for this project and have discussed them with my student.

Parent's Signature _____

Student's Name _____

Class Period _____

Make History

1. Working in a small group, interview several adults to find out how their lives have been affected by the development of faster and more powerful computers over the years. If possible, make an audiotape or videotape recording of each interview.

2. Research important events in the history of computers—for example, the development of the semiconductor and the Internet. Be sure to find out how scientists and other researchers have achieved dramatic increases in the speed of computers (as measured by the number of calculations that can be performed in a certain amount of time) and in the amount of information that computers can store.

3. Decide how the group will present the information group members have gathered about the history of computers. You might consider doing one of the following.

   • Make an illustrated timeline.

   • Create an interactive museum exhibit.

   • Conduct additional interviews. Then write a newspaper article or put together a radio or TV documentary about people's attitudes toward computers.

4. Make your presentation to the rest of the class at a time designated by the teacher.

To: The Parents of _____

Make History

Your student is about to start Chapter 9 in Algebra 1. In this chapter, your student will be studying polynomials. During the study of this chapter, your student will be working on a project about the history of computers. The following is a list of activities your student must complete for this project.

1. Working in a small group, your student will interview several adults to find out how their lives have been affected by the development of faster and more powerful computers over the years. If possible, students should make an audiotape or videotape recording of each interview.

2. Your student will research important events in the history of computers—for example, the development of the semiconductor and the Internet. He or she will find out how scientists and other researchers have achieved dramatic increases in the speed of computers (as measured by the number of calculations that can be performed in a certain amount of time) and in the amount of information that computers can store.

3. Group members will decide how to present the information they have gathered about the history of computers. They might consider doing one of the following.

   • Make an illustrated timeline.

   • Create an interactive museum exhibit.

   • Conduct additional interviews. Then write a newspaper article or put together a radio or TV documentary about people's attitudes toward computers.

4. Your student's group will make its presentation to the rest of the class at a time designated by the teacher.

Your student's project is due on _____ .

Please sign and return the bottom portion by _____ .

I have read the requirements for this project and have discussed them with my student.

Parent's Signature _____

Student's Name _____

Class Period _____

9

Chapter 9 Project B

Endangered Species

1. Animal populations develop polynomially. That is, if one animal has x offspring, then it will have an average of x^2 grandoffspring, x^3 great-grandoffspring, x^4 great-great-grandoffspring, and so on, assuming that each animal has an average of x babies in its lifetime. We can represent the number of descendants of one animal with the polynomial $x + x^2 + x^3 + x^4 + \cdots$, continuing for any number of generations and assuming that none of the animals dies early. So, if an animal has an average of 13 offspring in its lifetime, then it will have about 30,940 descendants in four generations. Complete the chart below for the deer population if each deer has an average of four offspring during its lifetime.

Generation	Polynomial	Number of Descendants
1	x	4
2	$x + x^2$	$4 + 16 = 20$
3	$x + x^2 + x^3$	$4 + 16 + 64 = $ _____
4	$x + x^2 + x^3 + x^4$	$4 + 16 + 64 + $ _____ $= $ _____
5	$x + x^2 + x^3 + x^4 + x^5$	$4 + 16 + 64 + $ _____ $ + $ _____ $= $ _____

2. Work in a small group. Choose two or more endangered species of animals. Do research to find out how and why they became endangered. Find out what is currently being done to protect the species to enable it to increase its numbers.

3. Find the average number of offspring each animal of each species has under normal conditions. Assume that each species can be protected and generate a population chart like the one in exercise 1 to find the number of animals that can be expected after 4, 5, and 6 generations. If this growth continues, in what generation do you think each species will be out of danger? Explain your answer.

4. Make posters summarizing your research and conclusions about each of your species. Present your posters to your class.

Chapter 9 Project B

To: The Parents of _____

Endangered Species

Your student is about to start Chapter 9 in Algebra 1. In this chapter, your student will be studying polynomials. During the study of this chapter, your student will be working on a project about endangered species of animals. The following is a list of activities your student must complete for this project.

1. Animal populations develop polynomially. That is, if one animal has x offspring, then it will have an average of x^2 grandoffspring, x^3 great-grandoffspring, x^4 great-great-grandoffspring, and so on, assuming that each animal has an average of x babies in its lifetime. We can represent the number of descendants of one animal with the polynomial $x + x^2 + x^3 + x^4 + \cdots$, continuing for any number of generations, assuming that none of the animals dies early. So, if an animal has an average of 13 offspring in its lifetime, then it will have about 30,940 descendants in four generations. Your student will complete the chart below for the deer population if each deer has an average of four offspring during its lifetime.

Generation	Polynomial	Number of Descendants
1	x	4
2	$x + x^2$	$4 + 16 = 20$
3	$x + x^2 + x^3$	$4 + 16 + 64 = $ _____
4	$x + x^2 + x^3 + x^4$	$4 + 16 + 64 + $ _____ $= $ _____
5	$x + x^2 + x^3 + x^4 + x^5$	$4 + 16 + 64 + $ _____ $+ $ _____ $= $ _____

2. Your student will work in a small group. Your student's group will choose two or more endangered animal species and will do research to find out how and why they became endangered. The group will find out what is currently being done to protect each species to enable it to increase its numbers.

3. Your student will find the average number of offspring each animal of each species has under normal conditions. He or she will assume that each species can be protected and generate a population chart like the one in exercise 1 to find the number of animals that can be expected after 4, 5, and 6 generations. Your student will state the number of generations he or she thinks must be born before each species will be out of danger. Your student will explain his or her answer.

4. Your student will make posters summarizing his or her research and conclusions about each of his or her species. Your student will present his or her posters to the class.

Your student's project is due on _____ .

Please sign and return the bottom portion by _____ .

I have read the requirements for this project and have discussed them with my student.

Parent's Signature _____

Student's Name _____

Class Period _____

NAME_____ DATE _____

Chapter 10 Project A

Movie Numbers

1. Numbers often appear in the titles of movies. Examples include *101 Dalmatians, Apollo 13,* and *Twelve Monkeys.* For this project, you will work in a small group to make a list of at least 20 such movies. Use newspaper movie listings for current films; visit a video store or consult a video catalogue for older titles.

2. Determine which of the numbers in your titles are prime and which are composite.

3. Find the prime factorization for each composite number in your list.

4. Create a board game in which players advance their game pieces by guessing movie titles with numbers in them. Write clues for each movie title you listed in exercise 1. For example, the clues for *Apollo 13* might be "Greek god of the sun" and "$1 \cdot 13$," and those for *Twelve Monkeys* might be "$2^2 \cdot 3$" and "small, lively primates that live together in social groups."

5. Exchange games with other groups and play them.

Chapter 10 Project A

To: The Parents of _____

Movie Numbers

Your student is about to start Chapter 10 in Algebra 1. In this chapter your student will study factoring. He or she will learn how to factor trinomials and use the distributive property, as well as solve equations by factoring. During the study of this chapter, your student will be working on a project about numbers in movie titles. The following is a list of activities your student must complete for this project.

1. Numbers often appear in the titles of movies. Examples include *101 Dalmatians, Apollo 13,* and *Twelve Monkeys.* For this project, your student will work in a small group to make a list of at least 20 such movies. He or she should use newspaper movie listings for current films and visit a video store or consult a video catalogue for older titles.

2. Your student will determine which of the numbers in the titles are prime and which are composite.

3. Your student will find the prime factorization for each composite number in his or her list.

4. Your student's group will create a board game in which players advance their game pieces by guessing movie titles with numbers in them. The group will write clues for each movie title listed in exercise 1. For example, the clues for *Apollo 13* might be "Greek god of the sun" and "$1 \cdot 13$," and those for *Twelve Monkeys* might be "$2^2 \cdot 3$" and "small, lively primates that live together in social groups."

5. Your student's group will exchange games with other groups and play them.

Your student's project is due on _____ .

Please sign and return the bottom portion by _____ .

I have read the requirements for this project and have discussed them with my student.

Parent's Signature _____

Student's Name _____

Class Period _____

Formulas for Success

1. In your life, you have used many formulas, especially in your study of math and science. Because you are something of an expert on formulas, the editor of a magazine has asked you and several other students to write an article entitled, "Twenty Really Useful Formulas." The purpose of this article is to show people that there are many practical applications of algebraic formulas. For example, the formula $h = -\frac{1}{2}gt^2 + v_0 + h_0$ can be used to find the height of an object, h, after the object has been traveling at a certain velocity, v, for a certain amount of time, t, from an initial height of h_0. Do research to find useful formulas. You might start by looking in math and science books. Collect as many formulas as possible.

2. Working in a small group, brainstorm ideas for formulas to include in your article. Vote on the 20 best, most useful formulas collected by members of your group.

3. Plan your article. After giving each formula, tell how it is used and show an example of its use. Be sure to consider the best way to present the information your group has gathered. Include graphics and photographs if you wish.

4. After your group has completed its article, trade articles with another group. Discuss how the articles are similar and different.

To: The Parents of _____

Formulas for Success

Your student is about to start Chapter 10 in Algebra 1. In this chapter, your student will be studying factors and factoring. The following is a list of activities your student must complete for this project.

1. Your student will suppose that the editor of a magazine has asked him or her and several other students to write an article entitled, "Twenty Really Useful Formulas." The purpose of this article is to show people that there are many practical applications of algebraic formulas. For example, the formula $h = -\frac{1}{2}gt^2 + v_0 + h_0$ can be used to find the height of an object, h, after the object has been traveling at a certain velocity, v, for a certain amount of time, t, from an initial height of h_0. Your student will do research to find useful formulas. He or she might start by looking in math and science books. Your student should collect as many formulas as possible.

2. Working in a small group, your student will brainstorm ideas for formulas to include in the article. Group members will vote on the 20 best, most useful formulas they have collected.

3. Group members will plan their article. After giving each formula, students should tell how it is used and show an example of its use. Students should consider the best way to present the information they have gathered. They can include graphics and photographs if they wish.

4. After group members have completed their article, they will trade articles with another group. Students will discuss how the articles are similar and different.

Your student's project is due on _____ .

Please sign and return the bottom portion by _____ .

I have read the requirements for this project and have discussed them with my student.

Parent's Signature _____

Student's Name _____

Class Period _____

Chapter 11 Project A

Volunteer Survey

1. Work with a partner to research and list organizations in your area that have volunteering opportunities. Possible places to check include health care organizations, schools, social service agencies, environmental programs, religious organizations, and museums.

2. Arrange the list you made in exercise 1 into different categories. Which categories have the most organizations listed? Which have the fewest?

3. Decide on a few organizations where you might be interested in volunteering. Interview a supervisor at one of these organizations to find out more about what the organization does. Find out how the organization uses its volunteers.

4. Find out how the organization uses the general equations for exponential growth and decay to make decisions about purchasing versus leasing, federal government funding, investments, population growth, and so on.

5. Write a newspaper article about volunteers and volunteering. At the end of your article, list different organizations that have volunteering opportunities and the phone numbers where people can get in touch with them.

To: The Parents of _____

Volunteer Survey

Your student is about to start Chapter 11 in Algebra 1. In this chapter, your student will be exploring quadratic and exponential functions. He or she will learn to solve problems involving growth and decay. During the study of this chapter your student will be working on a project about volunteer organizations. The following is a list of activities your student must complete for this project.

1. Your student will work with a partner to research and list organizations in the area that have volunteering opportunities. Possible places for them to check include health care organizations, schools, social service agencies, environmental programs, religious organizations, and museums.

2. Your student will arrange the list made in exercise 1 into different categories and determine which categories have the most organizations listed and which have the fewest.

3. Your student and his or her partner will decide on a few organizations where they might be interested in volunteering. They will interview a supervisor at one of these organizations to find out more about what the organization does and how it uses its volunteers.

4. The pair will find out how the organization uses the general equations for exponential growth and decay to make decisions about purchasing versus leasing, federal government funding, investments, population growth, and so on.

5. Your student and his or her partner will write a newspaper article about volunteers and volunteering. At the end of the article, they will list different organizations that have volunteering opportunities and the phone numbers where people can get in touch with them.

Your student's project is due on _____ .

Please sign and return the bottom portion by _____ .

I have read the requirements for this project and have discussed them with my student.

Parent's Signature _____

Student's Name _____

Class Period _____

11 Chapter 11 Project B

Constructing Parabolas

Materials: long piece of string
 lead fishing weights
 large piece of posterboard

1. When you hang a cable between two supports and then attach weights at equal intervals along the cable, the curve of the cable has the shape of a parabola. In this project, you will work in a small group to find out how engineers use parabolic curves in the design of suspension bridges. Begin by researching the history of suspension bridges.

2. Use the materials listed above to construct a model of a suspension bridge. Begin by tying each end of your string to two supports that are the same distance apart as the length of the posterboard. The string should hang down loosely. Place the posterboard behind the string and trace the curve on the posterboard.

3. Tie several lead fishing weights at equal intervals on the string. Draw the resulting parabolic curve on the posterboard. Answer the following questions.

   • How do the weights affect the curve?

   • How do you think adding more weights at equal intervals would affect the curve? Explain.

4. Use your research from exercise 1 and the results of your investigation with the string and weights to design the entry for "suspension bridge" in a multimedia encyclopedia.

Chapter 11 Project B

To: The Parents of _____

Constructing Parabolas

Your student is about to start Chapter 11 in Algebra 1. In this chapter, your student will be exploring quadratic and exponential functions. During the study of this chapter, your student will be working on a project about suspension bridges. The following is a list of activities your student must complete for this project.

Materials: long piece of string
lead fishing weights
large piece of posterboard

1. When you hang a cable between two supports and then attach weights at equal intervals along the cable, the curve of the cable has the shape of a parabola. In this project, your student will work in a small group to find out how engineers use parabolic curves in the design of suspension bridges. Group members will begin by researching the history of suspension bridges.

2. Your student's group will use the materials listed above to construct a model of a suspension bridge. Students will begin by tying each end of the string to two supports that are the same distance apart as the length of the posterboard. The string will hang down loosely. Group members will place the posterboard behind the piece of string and trace the parabola on the posterboard.

3. Group members will tie several lead fishing weights at equal intervals on the string. They will draw the resulting parabolic curve on the posterboard. Your student will answer the following questions.

   • How do the weights affect the curve?

   • How do you think adding more weights at equal intervals would affect the curve? Explain.

4. Your student's group will use the research from exercise 1 and the results of the investigation with the string and weights to design the entry for "suspension bridge" in a multimedia encyclopedia.

Your student's project is due on _____ .

Please sign and return the bottom portion by _____ .

I have read the requirements for this project and have discussed them with my student.

Parent's Signature   _____

Student's Name   _____

Class Period   _____

NAME_____ DATE _____

Chapter 12 Project A

Mayan Time

1. The Maya were a Native American people whose complex civilization reached a peak during the years from about 250 to 900. For this project, you will work with a small group to research Mayan civilization. Investigate such topics as art and architecture, mathematics and astronomy, religion, and way of life.

2. Using careful astronomical observations, the Maya developed a solar calendar. They also developed a sacred calendar that ran simultaneously with it. Research these two calendars to find out the answers to the following questions.

   • How many days made up a year in the solar calendar?
   • How were the days of the solar calendar divided into months?
   • How many days made up a year in the sacred calendar?
   • How were the days of the sacred calendar named?

3. Use the information you found about the number of days in each calendar to determine how many days would pass before a given day of the sacred calendar coincided with the same day of the solar calendar again. How many years on each calendar would pass before the calendars reached the same point again? Explain how these problems relate to the concept of the least common multiple. Make up some other problems using your knowledge of the Mayan calendars and exchange them with other groups to solve.

4. With your group, design a museum exhibit about the Mayan civilization. Include a timeline that would show how the two calendars correspond. Share your timelines with other groups.

To: The Parents of _____

Mayan Time

Your student is about to start Chapter 12 in Algebra 1. In this chapter your student will be exploring rational expressions and equations. He or she will learn to simplify, add, subtract, multiply, and divide rational expressions. During the study of this chapter, your student will be working on a project about the Maya. The following is a list of activities your student must complete for this project.

1. The Maya were a Native American people whose complex civilization reached a peak during the years from about 250 to 900. For this project, your student will work with a small group to research Mayan civilization. The group will investigate such topics as art and architecture, mathematics and astronomy, religion, and way of life.

2. Using careful astronomical observations, the Maya developed a solar calendar. They also developed a sacred calendar that ran simultaneously with it. Your student's group will research these two calendars to find out the answers to the following questions.

   • How many days made up a year in the solar calendar?
   • How were the days of the solar calendar divided into months?
   • How many days made up a year in the sacred calendar?
   • How were the days of the sacred calendar named?

3. Your student will use the information he or she found about the number of days in each calendar to determine how many days would pass before a given day of the sacred calendar coincided with the same day of the solar calendar again. He or she will also determine how many years on each calendar would pass before the calendars reached the same point again. Your student's group will explain how these problems relate to the concept of the least common multiple. They will make up some other problems using their knowledge of the Mayan calendars and exchange them with other groups to solve.

4. Your student's group will design a museum exhibit about the Mayan civilization. They will include a timeline that will show how the two calendars correspond. They will share their timelines with other groups.

Your student's project is due on _____ .

Please sign and return the bottom portion by _____ .

I have read the requirements for this project and have discussed them with my student.

Parent's Signature _____

Student's Name _____

Class Period _____

Get Focused!

Materials:

- convex lens (magnifying glass or eyeglasses)
- white posterboard cut into a 10 cm-by-10 cm square
- meterstick
- tape
- light source (window, lamp, flashlight)

1. Do research to find out about the focal length of a lens. Be sure to record any important formulas used when finding focal length. Also make copies of any important drawings associated with focal length.

2. Work in a small group to conduct the following experiment involving the focal length of a lens. Conduct the experiment several times to be sure your results are accurate.

   a. Tape the square of posterboard perpendicular to one end of the meterstick. Point the other end of the meterstick at the light source.

   b. Move the lens along the meterstick until the image of the light source appears upside down on the screen. Record the distance from the lens to the screen and the distance from the light source to the lens.

   c. Calculate the focal point of the lens. Use the equation $f(x) = \dfrac{d_i\, d_o}{(d_o + d_i)}$, where f is the focal length, d_i is the distance between the lens and light source, and d_o is the distance between the lens and the screen.

3. Write a report about your research and experiment. Be sure to include any important drawings in your report. Compare your findings with those of other groups.

Chapter 12 Project B

To: The Parents of _____

Get Focused!

Your student is about to start Chapter 12 in Algebra 1. In this chapter, your student will be exploring rational expressions and equations. During the study of this chapter, your student will be working on a project about the focal length of a lens. The following is a list of activities your student must complete for this project.

Your student will need the following materials.

- convex lens (magnifying glass or eyeglasses)
- white posterboard cut into a 10 cm-by-10 cm square
- meterstick
- tape
- light source (window, lamp, flashlight)

1. Your student will do research to find out about focal length. Your student should be sure to record any important formulas used when finding focal length. He or she should also make copies of any important drawings associated with focal length.

2. Your student will work in a small group to conduct the following experiment involving the focal length of a lens. The group will conduct the experiment several times to be sure its results are accurate.

   a. Group members will tape the square of posterboard perpendicular to one end of the meterstick. One student will point the other end of the meterstick at the light source.

   b. One group member will move the lens along the meterstick until the image of the light source appears upside down on the screen. Students will record the distance between the lens and the screen and the distance between the light source and the lens.

   c. Your student will calculate the focal point of the lens. He or she will use the equation $f(x) = \dfrac{d_i \, d_o}{(d_o + d_i)}$, where f is the focal length, d_i is the distance between the lens and light source, and d_o is the distance between the lens and the screen.

3. Your student will write a report about his or her research and experiment. Your student should be sure to include any important drawings in his or her report. Each group will compare its findings with those of other groups.

Your student's project is due on _____ .

Please sign and return the bottom portion by _____ .

I have read the requirements for this project and have discussed them with my student.

Parent's Signature _____

Student's Name _____

Class Period _____

Chapter 13 Project A

Radical Survey

1. Although you may not have thought about it, your parents and other adults you know probably spent time as teenagers studying math just as you are doing now. For this project, you will work in a small group to survey adults about their high school years and their experiences with math during and after high school. Begin by brainstorming a list of questions. Some possibilities are shown below.

   • What was high school like in your day?

   • What issues concerned you in high school?

   • What is your view of today's high schools?

   • Were your experiences with math in high school positive or negative? Explain your answer.

   • How do you or someone you work with use math on the job?

2. Design a questionnaire containing the five best questions from exercise 1. Distribute copies of your questionnaire to at least 20 adults. Be sure to explain the procedure for returning the completed questionnaires.

3. Make charts and graphs to organize and explain the data you and your group collected in exercise 2.

4. Use the data your group collected to prepare a newspaper article or a radio or TV report about adults and their experiences in high school.

Chapter 13 Project A

To: The Parents of _____

Radical Survey

Your student is about to start Chapter 13 in Algebra 1. In this chapter your student will be exploring radical expressions and equations. He or she will learn to use the Pythagorean theorem, simplify radical expressions, and solve problems involving radical equations. During the study of this chapter, your student will be working on a project about adults' high school experiences. The following is a list of activities your student must complete for this project.

1. Your student will work in a small group to survey you and other adults he or she knows about their high school years and their experiences with math during and after high school. With his or her group, your student will begin by brainstorming a list of questions. Some possibilities are shown below.

   • What was high school like in your day?

   • What issues concerned you in high school?

   • What is your view of today's high schools?

   • Were your experiences with math in high school positive or negative? Explain your answer.

   • How do you or someone you work with use math on the job?

2. Your student's group will design a questionnaire containing the five best questions from exercise 1. The group will distribute copies of the questionnaire to at least 20 adults and explain the procedure for returning the completed questionnaires.

3. Your student's group will make charts and graphs to organize and explain the data collected in exercise 2.

4. Your student will use the data collected to prepare a newspaper article or a radio or TV report about adults and their experiences in high school.

Your student's project is due on _____ .

Please sign and return the bottom portion by _____ .

I have read the requirements for this project and have discussed them with my student.

Parent's Signature _____

Student's Name _____

Class Period _____

Spirals

Materials: ruler, unlined paper

1. Decide on a unit length such as 1 centimeter. Construct a right triangle with both legs equal to the unit length. Then use the hypotenuse of the first triangle as the leg of a second right triangle. The other leg should have a measure of 1 unit. Use the hypotenuse of the second triangle as the leg of a third right triangle. Again, the other leg should have a measure of 1 unit. Continue in this way to draw as many connected right triangles as you can. Be as precise as possible in your measuring and use a sharp pencil.

2. Copy and complete a chart like the following for the right triangles you have drawn. Use the Pythagorean theorem to find the missing lengths.

Triangle	Leg	Leg	Hypotenuse
First	1 unit	1 unit	$\sqrt{2}$ units
Second	$\sqrt{2}$ units	1 unit	?
Third	?	1 unit	?
.	.	.	.
.	.	.	.
.	.	.	.

3. The figure you have produced is a spiral. Find actual examples of spirals that appear in nature, or look for photographs or illustrations of spirals in magazines. The petals of many flowers are arranged in a spiral shape. Other examples include the seedhead of a sunflower, shells, pine cones, pineapples, and strands of DNA. You may also wish to look for examples of spirals in art or architecture.

4. Choose one of the following ways of presenting your work.

   - Make a poster of the drawing you made and pictures of spirals in nature, art, or architecture.
   - Give an oral presentation that includes actual examples of spirals.
   - Plan an activity involving spirals.

Chapter 13 Project B

To: The Parents of _____

Spirals

Your student is about to start Chapter 13 in Algebra 1. In this chapter, your student will be using the Pythagorean theorem to solve problems, simplifying radical expressions, solving radical equations, and solving quadratic equations by completing the square. During the study of this chapter, your student will be working on a project about spirals and the Pythagorean theorem. The following is a list of activities your student must complete for this project.

1. Your student will begin by choosing a unit length such as 1 centimeter. With a ruler and unlined paper, your student will construct a right triangle with both legs equal to the unit length. Then your student will use the hypotenuse of the first triangle as the leg of a second right triangle. The other leg should have a measure of 1 unit. Your student should continue in this way to draw as many connected right triangles as possible on the paper. The drawings should be as precise as possible.

2. Your student will use the Pythagorean theorem to find the missing lengths of right triangles and then record the results in a chart.

Triangle	Leg	Leg	Hypotenuse
First	1 unit	1 unit	$\sqrt{2}$ units
Second	$\sqrt{2}$ units	1 unit	?
Third	?	1 unit	?
·	·	·	·
·	·	·	·
·	·	·	·

3. The figure produced will be a spiral. Your student should find actual examples of spirals that appear in nature, or he or she should look for photographs or illustrations of spirals in magazines. The petals of many flowers are arranged in a spiral shape. Other examples include the seedhead of a sunflower, shells, pine cones, pineapples, and strands of DNA. Your student may also wish to look for examples of spirals in art or architecture.

4. Your student will choose one of the following ways of presenting his or her work.

   • Make a poster of the drawing you made and pictures of spirals in nature, art, or architecture.
   • Give an oral presentation that includes actual examples of spirals.
   • Plan an activity involving spirals.

Your student's project is due on _____ .

Please sign and return the bottom portion by _____ .

I have read the requirements for this project and have discussed them with my student.

Parent's Signature _____

Student's Name _____

Class Period _____